KYLE THOMAS

Guardian
OF THE
Realm

WRITTEN BY: KYLE THOMAS,
LEAH MOORE & JOHN REPPION

ARTWORK BY: AMCO STUDIO

MICHAEL  JOSEPH

THIS BOOK IS DEDICATED TO MY MUM.
THANK YOU FOR YOUR UNCONDITIONAL
LOVE AND SUPPORT THROUGHOUT
THIS JOURNEY AND CHAMPIONING ME
TO MAKE MY DREAMS A REALITY.

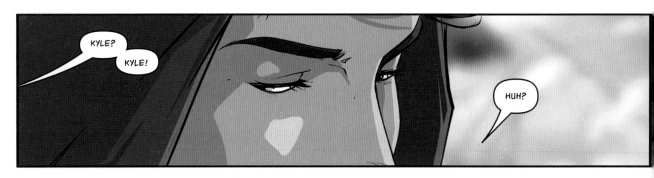

WELL, WHAT DO YOU THINK?

IT'S... NOT REALLY WHAT I IMAGINED...

WAIT, WHAT'S THAT KID DOING?

HEY!

COME BACK HERE!

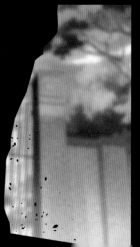

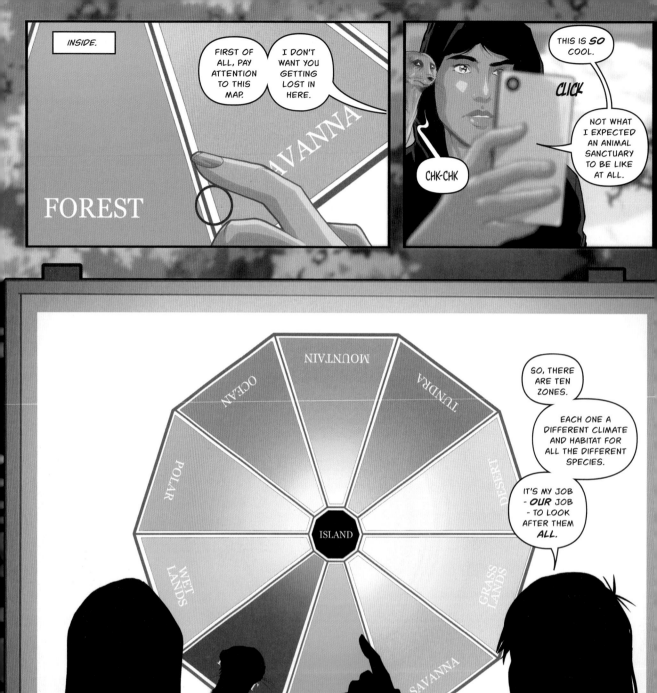

HA. NO, NOT REALLY...

WELL, ACTUALLY, YEAH, I SUPPOSE I *KIND* OF DO.

I GUESS I *LIVE* THERE NOW. ME AND MY MUM. SHE'S THE GUARDIAN.

GUARDIAN?

YEAH, THAT'S WHAT THE PERSON IN CHARGE OF THE PLACE IS CALLED, APPARENTLY. SOUNDS KIND OF WEIRD, I KNOW.

I THINK IT SOUNDS COOL.

YEAH. YEAH, I GUESS IT *IS* KIND OF COOL.

HELLO, MYLO...

PRRRRUP

HE LIKES YOU.

WELL, I'D BETTER GET ON.

I'VE GOT LOADS MORE POSTERS TO DO.

YOU GOING TO COME BY? WE COULD DO WITH THE HELP.

OH, I... I-I DON'T KNOW.

MAYBE, YEAH.

IF I HAVE TIME, YOU KNOW?

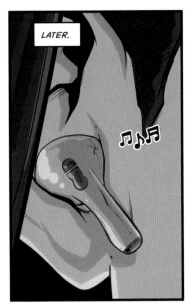

LATER.

♪♫♬

♪♫♬ ♫♫♬

WHO *IS* THAT?

CHITT-TIKK?

AH, YOUNG MISTER THOMAS.

THERE YOU ARE.

I'M SORRY, DO I KNOW YOU?

HOW *UNFORTUNATE.*

NO MATTER.

I'M SURE WE SHALL RUN INTO EACH OTHER AGAIN.

SOON.

WOW.

W-WHAT WAS *THAT* ALL ABOUT?

NEVER MIND THAT NOW.

YOU WERE SUPPOSED TO BE BACK *AGES* AGO.

I THOUGHT I'D JUST GRAB A SNACK ON THE WAY...

WELL, HURRY UP! THEY'RE WAITING.

WHO ARE?

THE *VOLUNTEERS,* OF COURSE!

A LITTLE LATER.

INCREDIBLE.

I MEAN, I'VE NEVER SEEN ANYTHING LIKE IT.

THIS IS AN *UNKNOWN* SPECIES OF CHAMELEON, I'M SURE OF IT.

THIS ZONE - THE RAINFOREST - SEEMS LIKE IT'S ONE OF THE MOST OVERGROWN, SO MAYBE WE SHOULD START HERE?

UNLESS ANYONE WANTS TO START SOMEWHERE ELSE?

I'D LIKE TO LOOK AROUND A BIT MORE.

YEAH, ME TOO. THIS PLACE IS *AMAZING.*

WELL, I GUESS JAK COULD START HERE, AND WE COULD MOVE ON.

IS THAT OKAY WITH YOU, JAK?

HUH? YEAH. YEAH, I'LL STAY HERE.

OKAY THEN, WE'LL SEE YOU LATER, YEAH?

SOON.

SO, YOU'RE OKAY HERE?

SNIK

YEAH, I'M FINE.

ALTHOUGH, I'M BEGINNING TO WISH I'D PICKED AN EASIER JOB, LIKE TAYLOR.

I'M SURE SHE'LL COME BACK HERE TO HELP IF SHE FINISHES AT THE MOUNTAIN ZONE.

I MEAN, *I* THINK THIS IS GOING TO TAKE *WEEKS*, TO BE HONEST.

HEY, WHAT'S WRONG, MYLO?

CHAKKA-TIKK-TIK-TIK!

HEY! WHERE ARE YOU GOING?

TIKKA-TIK-TIKK-*PRRRRUP!*

HEY, DEE, HOW ARE YOU GETTING ON?

OH, HI.

YEAH, NOT BAD.

HEY, YOU LOOK...

DID YOU DO SOMETHING TO YOUR HAIR, OR SOMETHING?

THAT'S WHAT *I* SAID!

YOU'VE DONE A *GREAT* JOB HERE, DEE.

WE WERE THINKING IT'S ABOUT TIME TO PACK UP FOR THE DAY.

COOL WITH ME.

YOU KNOW, I'D *SWEAR* THERE'S SOMETHING...

... *DIFFERENT* ABOUT YOU, KYLE.

OH, SORRY, I... I, UHM, DIDN'T GET ALL THAT MUCH DONE.

I GOT A BIT *DISTRACTED.* LOST TRACK OF TIME.

NEVER MIND, JAK, THERE'S ALWAYS TOMORROW.

COME ON.

LET'S GET RID OF THIS STUFF.

SOON.

THAT'S THE LAST OF THEM.

FANTASTIC.

WELL, WE'D LIKE TO THANK YOU *ALL* FOR ALL YOUR HARD WORK TODAY, WOULDN'T WE, KYLE?

YEAH. DEFINITELY.

THANKS, EVERYONE!

THIS WORLD-
THE WORLD WE
LIVE IN - IS THE
HUMAN WORLD,
RIGHT?

BUT THERE'S
MORE TO IT THAN
THAT. MORE THAN
WHAT MOST
PEOPLE SEE
EVERY DAY.

THERE ARE OTHER
WORLDS - **REALMS,**
WE CALL THEM -
RIGHT NEXT TO OUR
OWN.

AND SOMETIMES,
IN SOME PLACES,
OUR WORLD AND
THOSE **OTHERS**
OVERLAP.

IT'S ALWAYS
BEEN THAT
WAY.

"OF COURSE,
PEOPLE WERE
AFRAID."

"THEY WANTED TO
FIGHT THE THINGS THAT
CROSSED OVER FROM
THE OTHER REALMS."

"BUT, A LONG TIME
AGO, SOMEONE
CHANGED ALL THAT."

THEY REALISED THAT
THESE WEREN'T
MONSTERS, THEY
WERE JUST ANIMALS,
AND THEY NEEDED TO
BE **PROTECTED.**

"THAT WAS THE
BEGINNING OF THE
GUARDIANS."

"THE FIRST SANCTUARIES WERE BUILT HUNDREDS AND HUNDREDS OF YEARS AGO."

"PLACES WHERE ANIMALS, WHOSE REALMS WERE UNDER THREAT, COULD BE KEPT SAFE."

THE GUARDIANS FOUND A WAY TO *DELIBERATELY* OPEN PORTALS TO THOSE REALMS.

USING *GEM-KEYS*.

GEMSTONES FOUND IN DIFFERENT REALMS COULD BE USED TO CONNECT *DIRECTLY* TO THOSE REALMS.

BUT *ONLY* IF THEY WERE USED WITH ONE OF THE *GUARDIAN-KEYS*, CREATED AND HELD BY THE GUARDIANS.

"IT MUST HAVE ALL SEEMED LIKE *MAGIC* TO THEM BACK THEN."

"CRAFTING THE GEM-KEYS, CREATING THE SANCTUARIES, FORGING THE WEAPONS TO PROTECT THE REALMS."

"OVER TIME IT BECAME A SCIENCE."

"TECHNOLOGY MOVED ON, THINGS CHANGED, AND THE GUARDIANS BECAME WHAT THEY ARE TODAY."

WHEN ME AND MYLO WERE WITH THE OTHER MEERKATS IN THEIR REALM, BEFORE YOU CAME, WE SAW...

ONE OF THEM HAD BEEN **BITTEN** BY THE VOID BEAST.

"HE WAS THERE ONE SECOND, AND THE NEXT HE WAS GONE."

"AS IF HE JUST **VANISHED** OUT OF EXISTENCE."

THAT'S **EXACTLY** WHAT HAPPENS.

BUT MINOR INJURIES CAN BE EVEN WORSE.

THE ANIMAL CAN BECOME **INFECTED.**

EVENTUALLY **BECOMING** A VOID BEAST THEMSELVES.

GULP

"THAT'S WHY THE REALMS, AND THEIR INHABITANTS, HAVE TO BE PROTECTED AT ALL COSTS."

"THE VOID BEASTS ARE **MORE** THAN JUST AN INVASIVE SPECIES."

"THEY'RE A **DISEASE.**"

BUT IT'S NOT JUST THE ANIMAL REALMS THAT ARE IN DANGER.

THE VOID BEASTS... WE THINK ONE OF THEM MIGHT HAVE CROSSED OVER.

ESCAPED.

INTO *OUR* WORLD.

WHAT?

THAT'S ONE OF THE REASONS WE'RE NEEDED HERE, *NOW*, AT THE SANCTUARY.

WE HAVE TO MAKE SURE NOTHING ELSE GETS THROUGH.

THIS IS A GUARDIAN-KEY.

WITHOUT IT, THE DOOR INTO THE OTHER REALMS HERE AT THE SANCTUARY CAN'T BE UNLOCKED, OR LOCKED.

THAT'S WHY I KEEP IT WITH ME. ALL THE TIME.

MUM, I WANT TO HELP!

NOW THAT I KNOW ALL THIS, I *CAN* HELP!

I COULD BE A GUARDIAN TOO!

I KNEW YOU'D SAY THAT.

BUT IT'S TOO DANGEROUS RIGHT NOW.

IT'S GETTING LATE. YOU SHOULD PROBABLY THINK ABOUT GETTING TO BED.

IT'S A LOT TO TAKE IN, AND IT'S BEEN A *LONG* DAY.

BED? BUT...

BUT, MUM, I'M NOT EVEN...

YAWN

...TIRED.

BED.

WE'LL TALK IN THE MORNING.

NEXT DAY.

GOOD MORNING, KYLE!

OH, ERM, YEAH, MORNING.

HA, YOU'D BETTER GET USED TO THAT.

ONCE YOU'VE CROSSED OVER INTO THE ANIMAL REALMS, THINGS ARE NEVER QUITE THE SAME.

YEAH, I... I CAN SEE THAT.

LOVELY DAY, ISN'T IT?

YEAH. NO... NO PROBLEM.

THANK YOU FOR YESTERDAY, KYLE.

RIGHT, LET'S SEE IF OUR VOLUNTEERS ARE READY FOR ANOTHER DAY'S CLEAN-UP, SHALL WE?

DEE. LOOKS LIKE YOU'RE THE FIRST ONE HERE.

OH! I...

YEAH, WELL, I WANTED TO... YOU KNOW.

ACTUALLY, I *THINK* I MIGHT HAVE LEFT SOMETHING BEHIND YESTERDAY.

I JUST NEED TO... I'LL JUST GO AND *CHECK*, YEAH?

WOW, SHE'S KEEN.

HMM.

HMM.

MORNING, ALL.

I THOUGHT I MIGHT BE A BIT EARLY BUT, UHM...

IT LOOKS LIKE DEE BEAT ME TO IT. HA.

YEAH, SHE SAID SHE LEFT SOMETHING...

ANYWAY, COME IN, JAK.

HEY, MYLO.

SNFF SNFF SNFF

DON'T WORRY ABOUT ME, I'LL GO AND GRAB SOME TOOLS AND STUFF AND MAKE A START.

I'LL MAKE UP FOR YESTERDAY, I PROMISE. JUST GOT A BIT DISTRACTED, YOU KNOW?

HEY, WHAT HAPPENED TO YOUR GLASSES?

MY GLASSES?

WHAT ABOUT MY...

HA. YEAH. OF COURSE.

HERE THEY ARE.

SILLY ME, EH?

WELL, I'D BETTER GET ON.

HANG ON!

DON'T LOCK THE GATE!

I NEED TO GET OUT AGAIN!

HEY!

WATCH IT!

SORRY.

I...I JUST DON'T FEEL TOO GOOD, SO I'M GOING TO HEAD BACK HOME.

SORRY.

WAIT A MINUTE AND I'LL DRIVE YOU HOME, DEE.

DID YOU FIND WHAT YOU WERE LOOKING FOR?

LOOKING FOR...? OH. YEAH. YEAH.

NO, THANKS, HONESTLY, IT'S FINE. I-I'LL CATCH A BUS.

DING DING DING DING DING DING

"THAT'S THE ALARM!"

"AGAIN?"

MUM, *WAIT!* I CAN *HELP!*

HEY! MY *DOUGHNUT!*

YOU STAY HERE! LOCK THOSE GATES! *I'LL* TAKE CARE OF THIS!

WOW, I *HATE* THAT ALARM THING! IT'S SO *LOUD!*

IS IT BROKEN, OR SOMETHING?

"SOMETHING LIKE THAT, YEAH."

"I JUST WISH MUM WOULD LET ME *HELP.*"

IT'S A *LOT* FOR HER TO DO ON HER OWN, YOU KNOW?

HEY, SHE'S *NOT* ON HER OWN.

KYLE, I'M *SURE* YOUR MUM REALLY APPRECIATES *EVERYTHING* YOU'RE DOING HERE.

AND, IF YOU WANT TO HELP, HELP *ME* WITH THESE.

LET'S FIND JAK, AND SEE WHAT FLAVOUR HE WANTS.

NUH-HUH, MYLO.

OH, *COME* ON!

SOON.

THIS LOOKS *AMAZING!*

HA. YOU'D THINK YOU'D NEVER SEEN A DOUGHNUT BEFORE!

PSSST

HUH?

PSSST

DOWN HERE!

I NEED TO TALK TO YOU!

ME? WHAT'S UP?

SOMETHING'S GOING ON. SOMETHING'S NOT RIGHT.

THE RAINFOREST GEM-KEY IS GONE!

GONE?

MUM MUST HAVE TAKEN IT. THE ALARM -

NO. THIS MORNING'S ALARM WASN'T FROM *THIS* ZONE.

WAIT, THEN WHERE -

HA. HAS THAT GIANT ARMADILLO GOT SOMETHING SHE WANTS TO TELL YOU?

DID YOU HEAR WHAT SHE SAID?

WHAT? NO, OF COURSE NOT. I... I WAS *JOKING.*

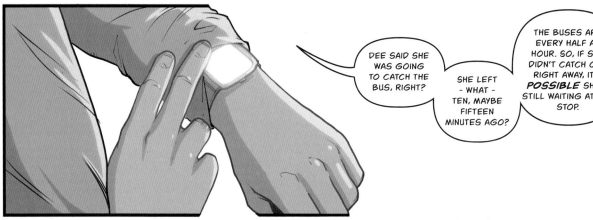

DEE SAID SHE WAS GOING TO CATCH THE BUS, RIGHT?

SHE LEFT - WHAT - TEN, MAYBE FIFTEEN MINUTES AGO?

THE BUSES ARE EVERY HALF AN HOUR. SO, IF SHE DIDN'T CATCH ONE RIGHT AWAY, IT'S *POSSIBLE* SHE'S STILL WAITING AT THE STOP.

YOU'RE *RIGHT!*

BUT I NEED TO *HURRY!*

HEY, I'M COMING TOO!

I... I'LL WAIT HERE.

CATCH!

WHUH?

"LOCK THE GATES AND WAIT FOR US."

"WE'LL BE BACK AS SOON AS WE CAN."

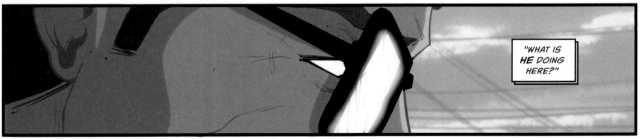

EASY NOW. WE'LL GET YOU INSIDE, SO YOU CAN REST.

DID... DID ONE OF THE ANIMALS DO THIS TO YOU?

YOU HEARD THE ALARM, EARLIER?

"WHEN THAT BELL RINGS - ALTHOUGH IT DOESN'T *ALWAYS* WORK - IT MEANS I'M NEEDED *ELSEWHERE*."

"I HAVE TO GO *BEYOND* THE SANCTUARY."

I HAD TO GO INTO THE MOUNTAIN REALM.

BUT I WASN'T THERE FOR LONG.

"I WAS PULLED OUT, INTO ANOTHER REALM."

"THE SAME THING HAPPENED YESTERDAY, WHEN YOU AND MYLO USED THE SAVANNA GEM-KEY, KYLE."

MUM, SHOULD YOU BE TALK -

IF THE GEM-KEYS ARE SWAPPED HERE, IT DOESN'T JUST OPEN A NEW DOOR.

IT WILL PULL A GUARDIAN FROM THE REALM THEY'RE IN, INTO THAT NEW ONE.

"KYLE, IS SHE OKAY?"

"I MEAN, SHE'S NOT REALLY MAKING SENSE."

"IT... IT **DOES** MAKE SENSE TO ME, TAYLOR."

"I CAN'T EXPLAIN IT TO YOU RIGHT NOW, BUT IT DOES."

TELL US WHAT **HAPPENED,** MUM.

HOW DID YOU GET HURT?

IT... IT MUST HAVE ALREADY BEEN THERE. **WAITING.**

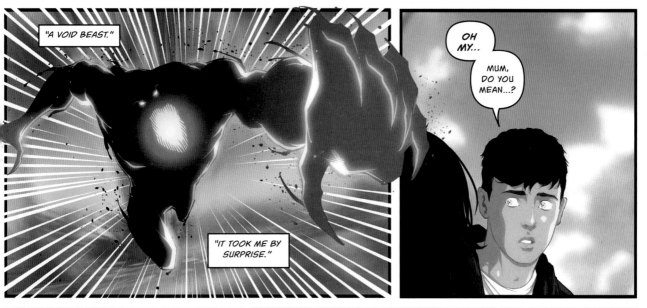

"A VOID BEAST."

"IT TOOK ME BY SURPRISE."

OH MY...

MUM, DO YOU MEAN...?

"IT **BIT** YOU?"

WHAT ARE YOU TWO TALKING ABOUT?

WHAT THE **HECK** IS A VOID BEAST?

WH-WHAT HAPPENS IF ONE BITES YOU?

WHAT HAPPENED?

MUM'S HURT.

DEE. YOU'RE BACK.

ARE YOU FEELING BETTER NOW?

I... UHM...

SHE WASN'T REALLY SICK, MUM.

THAT WAS A LIE.

DID YOU BRING BACK WHAT YOU *STOLE?*

DID YOU BRING THE RAINFOREST GEM-KEY?

THE *WHAT?*

I DIDN'T STEAL ANY *KEY-THING,* I-I JUST *BORROWED* –

ME!

SHE JUST BORROWED ME!

WOW, SHE'S... SHE'S *REALLY* CHATTY ALL OF A SUDDEN.

GRNK GRN GRN GRNK-NK

WE, ERM, SORT OF MADE FRIENDS WHEN I WAS WORKING ON THE FOREST ZONE YESTERDAY.

I KNOW IT WAS *STUPID* OF ME TO TAKE HER HOME. I'M REALLY SORRY.

I DIDN'T THINK ANYONE WOULD NOTICE. I'VE NEVER HAD A PET...

I REALISED I NEEDED STRAW OR SOMETHING, TO KEEP HER WARM, SO I GRABBED SOME THIS MORNING.

GRUNK GRUNK NNNNG NG NG

OKAY, OKAY, *ENOUGH.* I CAN'T UNDERSTAND ANYTHING IF YOU'RE *BOTH* TALKING AT ONCE.

WAIT, NOW I'M *REALLY* CONFUSED.

I THOUGHT IT WAS SOME *GEM-THING* DEE WAS SUPPOSED TO HAVE TAKEN, NOT A *HEDGEHOG.*

YOU ASKED DEE IF SHE'D BROUGHT THE RAINFOREST KEY BACK?

IT WAS THE RAINFOREST REALM WHERE I WAS ATTACKED!

"BUT, MUM, THAT MEANS THAT THE GEM-KEY **WAS** HERE ALL ALONG."

"AND SOMEONE - **OR SOMETHING** - SWITCHED IT AND THE MOUNTAIN ONE WHILE YOU WERE IN THE REALMS."

OH MY...!

IT'S **GONE.**

"THE **GUARDIAN-KEY** IS GONE!"

OH, THIS IS **BAD.**

THIS IS **REALLY** BAD.

I'M **REALLY** SORRY, BUT I'M **COMPLETELY** LOST HERE.

GUARDIAN-KEYS? VOID BEASTS? REALMS?

YEAH, I-I HAVE TO SAY, I DON'T **REALLY** UNDERSTAND EITHER.

THERE'S NO **TIME**... FOR ALL THIS.

I'VE... I'VE **GOT** TO GET THAT KEY BACK.

NO, MUM, YOU CAN'T GO **ANYWHERE**.

YOU TOLD ME THAT IF SOMEONE GETS BITTEN BY A VOID BEAST THEY CAN EITHER DISAPPEAR, OR...

...OR THEY GET **INFECTED**.

I'M A **GUARDIAN**, KYLE.

THERE ARE SPECIAL OLD REMEDIES - **POTIONS** AND MEDICINES AND THINGS - HERE AT THE SANCTUARY FOR THESE KINDS OF EMERGENCIES.

BUT THAT'S NOT - **MUMPH**

I'LL BE **FINE**. I PROMISE.

I MEAN... I *ALSO* HAVE ABSOLUTELY NO CLUE WHAT YOU AND KYLE ARE TALKING ABOUT AT THIS POINT.

BUT I *DO* KNOW THAT YOU *DEFINITELY* SHOULDN'T BE GOING ANYWHERE, BESIDES *HOSPITAL,* WITH AN ANIMAL BITE LIKE THAT.

WITHOUT THE GUARDIAN-KEY, THE DOOR INTO THE OTHER REALMS CAN'T BE CLOSED.

ANYTHING COULD COME THROUGH.

BUT THAT'S NOT THE WORST OF IT. IF THE KEY FELL INTO THE WRONG HANDS...

"IF THE VOID BEASTS FOUND IT..."

"IT COULD BE THE END."

"OF *EVERYTHING.*"

I *HAVE* TO HELP THIS TIME, MUM.

I *CAN* DO IT.

"*WE* CAN DO IT."

MEANWHILE...

RAINFOREST REALM.

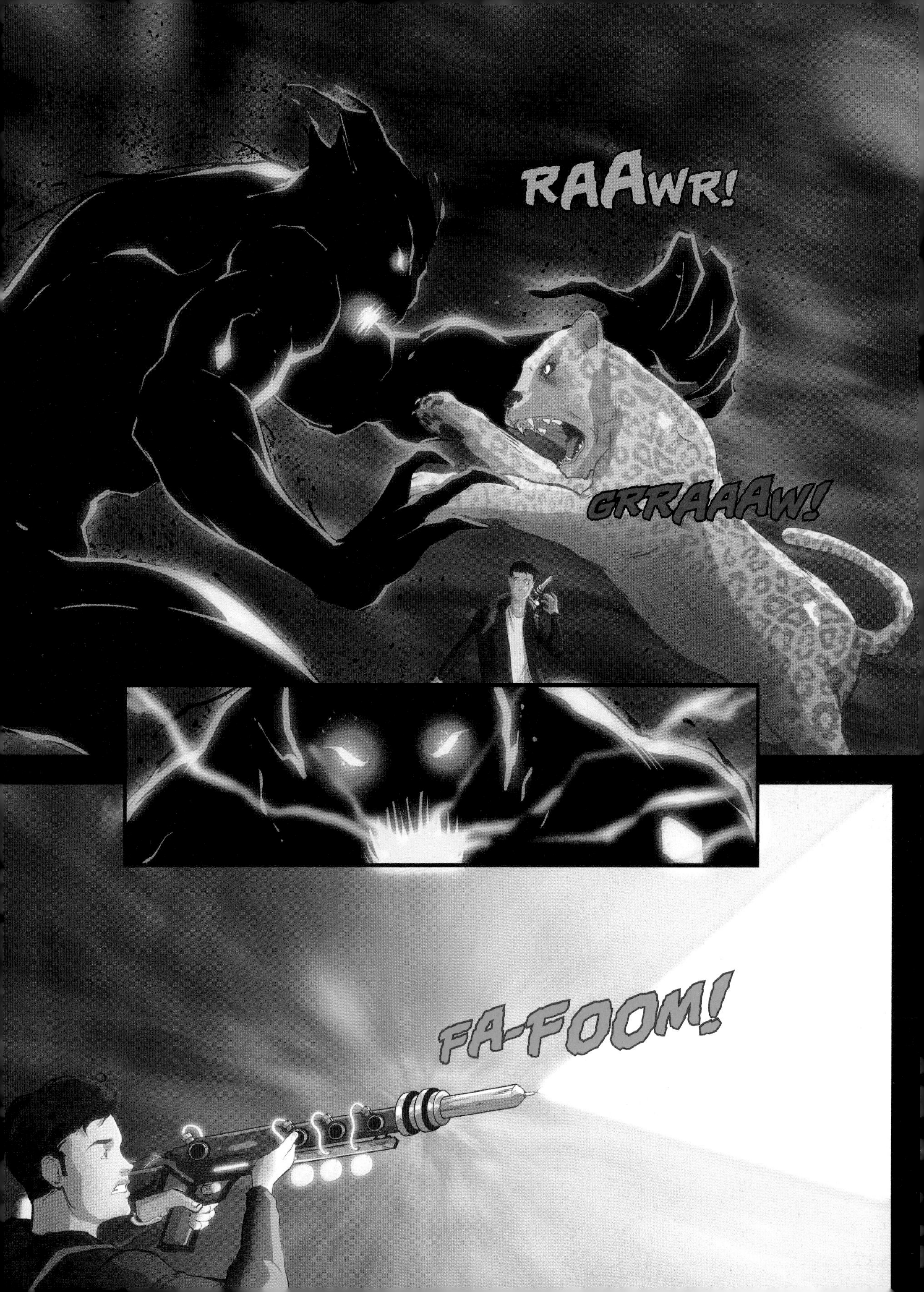
RAAWR!
GRRAAAAW!
FA-FOOM!

SKREEEEEE

SKREEEEEE

WOW.

I GUESS THAT'S HOW *THAT* WORKS.

I-IS EVERYONE OKAY?

DID YOU JUST *DISINTEGRATE* THAT THING?

WAS *THAT* ONE OF THOSE *VOID BEAST* THINGS YOU WERE TALKING ABOUT?

GUARDIAN, YOU SAVED MY LIFE.

THANK YOU.

...ELDRETH WOULD KNOW...

... BUT, I'M SORRY, I...

... DON'T KNOW WHERE...

... TO FIND HER.

YOU'RE, ERM, YOU'RE WELCOME.

MR SLOTH, YOU SAID YOU KNEW WHO WE NEEDED TO SPEAK TO?

ABOUT THE CURE?

YES...

YOUNG GUARDIAN, I AM IN YOUR DEBT.

I KNOW WHERE ELDRETH'S NEST LIES.

I CAN LEAD YOU TO HER.

THAT WAS A STRAIGHT-UP MONSTER YOU JUST BLASTED INTO NOTHINGNESS!

AND YOUR MUM SAID NOT TO SPLIT UP, BUT JAK'S GONE! HE'S DISAPPEARED!

WAIT, WE'RE NOT HERE - WHEREVER WE ARE - TO FIND THIS CURE THING, ARE WE?

WE'RE SUPPOSED TO BE LOOKING FOR THE MAGIC GEM-KEY THAT THE TALKING SLOTH SAID WASHED AWAY IN THE RIVER!

"OKAY, OKAY, LISTEN, I GUESS IT'S TIME I EXPLAINED SOME STUFF TO YOU."

"THIS PLACE WHERE WE ARE, IT'S CALLED A REALM."

"THE REALMS KIND OF SIT NEXT TO OUR OWN WORLD, BUT THEY'RE DIFFERENT."

"AND CROSSING OVER INTO THEM MAKES PEOPLE DIFFERENT."

"THE SANCTUARY IS A KIND OF GATEWAY."

"THE GEM-KEYS FROM THE DIFFERENT ZONES OPEN UP DIFFERENT REALMS."

"BUT THE GATEWAY CAN'T BE UNLOCKED OR LOCKED WITHOUT THE GUARDIAN-KEY."

"AND THEY'RE DANGEROUS. REALLY DANGEROUS."

"YES, WE HAVE TO FIND THE GUARDIAN-KEY."

"AND, YES, WE NEED TO FIND JAK."

"HERE ANIMALS CAN TALK."

"WE CAN UNDERSTAND THEM, AND THEY CAN UNDERSTAND US."

"THAT'S WHAT MUM LOST HERE, WHEN SHE WAS ATTACKED."

"BY A VOID BEAST."

"THEY COME FROM SOMEWHERE ELSE – SOMEWHERE OUTSIDE."

"BUT MOST OF ALL NOW, I NEED TO SPEAK TO THIS ELDRETH."

"BECAUSE IT MIGHT BE THE ONLY CHANCE I HAVE TO SAVE MUM."

"I'LL EXPLAIN MORE ON THE WAY."

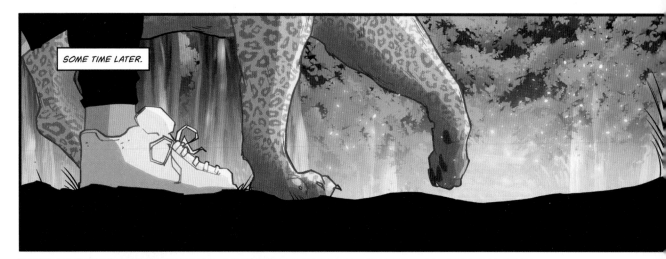

SOME TIME LATER.

WE ARE HERE.

SEE, ELDRETH SLEEPS.

I DON'T SEE ANYONE...

DO WE NEED TO WAIT FOR NIGHT, OR SOMETHING?

DAY AND NIGHT, SHE SLEEPS.

FOR YEARS AND YEARS AND YEARS.

I WAS JUST A CUB WHEN LAST I HEARD HER SPEAK.

I HOPE SHE IS WELL RESTED.

"MY MUM."

"SHE'S HURT."

SHE'S A GUARDIAN, AND SHE WAS BITTEN.

BY A VOID BEAST.

I SEE. I AM SORRY.

BUT WHAT CAN I DO TO HELP?

"I WAS TOLD THAT THERE WAS A WAY TO HELP HER. A CURE."

"AND THAT YOU KNEW WHERE IT COULD BE FOUND."

I KNOW MANY THINGS, I REMEMBER MANY THINGS.

BUT THE PLACE YOU SEEK HAS BEEN SHUNNED FOR HUNDREDS OF YEARS.

"THE LOST CITY."

"LOST TO THEM FOR LONGER THAN EVEN I CAN REMEMBER."

"THE CREATURES YOU SPOKE OF - LIKE THE ONE WHICH INJURED YOUR MOTHER - THEY GATHER THERE."

"THEY ARE DRAWN TO THE PLACE."

I HEARD IT SAID, LONG AGO, THAT THE CURE LIES AT THE HEART OF THE CITY.

A SPRING WHOSE WATERS HAVE THE POWER TO HEAL THOSE AFFLICTED WITH THE VOID BEAST'S BITE.

"PERHAPS THAT IS WHY THEY CONGREGATE THERE."

"OR PERHAPS THERE IS SOME OTHER REASON."

THE LOST CITY LIES...

WHAT'S THAT YOU SAY?

SPEAK UP! MY OLD EARS ARE NOT WHAT THEY USED TO BE.

"YOU HAVE LOST YOUR GEM- KEY, GUARDIAN?"

"MY WINGED FRIEND HERE SAYS IT HAS BEEN FOUND."

SHE SAYS SHE CAN LEAD YOU TO IT.

AND TO THE LOST CITY.

AND SO...

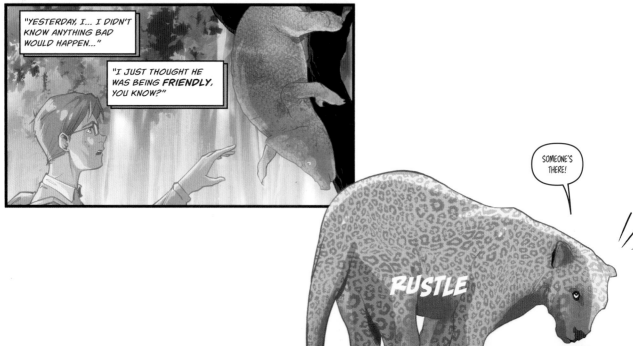

"IT... IT'S THE **CHAMELEON**. FROM THE SANCTUARY."

"WE KIND OF SHOOK HANDS AND THEN..."

"... AND THEN HE WAS **ME**."

"**LOOKED** LIKE ME, I MEAN."

IT SEEMED **COOL**, YOU KNOW?

LIKE **MAGIC**.

I, ERM, I EVEN GAVE HIM MY SPARE PAIR OF GLASSES TO WEAR.

I... DON'T REALLY KNOW WHY...

"HE SAID HE'D SHOW ME WHERE HE CAME FROM."

"HE GRABBED THIS **GEM-THING**. WE WENT TO THE ISLAND ZONE."

"SORRY, I KNOW YOUR MUM SAID NOT TO..."

"THERE WAS THIS **WEIRD** DOOR. ALL THESE **COLOURS**."

THEN WE... **SOMEHOW**... WE ENDED UP HERE.

AND IT WAS **AMAZING**.

LIKE A **DREAM**, YOU KNOW?

BUT... THEN WE SAW THIS **THING**... LIKE A **MONSTER**.

"WE HID, BUT THEN HE STARTED ACTING ALL **WEIRD**."

"HE SAID HE'D BEEN **BITTEN**..."

"THAT HE DIDN'T WANT ME TO GET BITTEN OR HURT..."

"BUT THAT HE COULDN'T CONTROL... **SOMETHING**... IT WAS TAKING HIM OVER."

HE TIED ME UP HERE.

HE SAID HE WAS **SORRY**. HE'D COME BACK.

BUT HE HAD THINGS... THINGS HE DIDN'T WANT TO DO, BUT HE HAD TO.

IT SORT OF SEEMED LIKE HE... COULDN'T HELP IT.

SO YESTERDAY, WHEN YOU SAID YOU GOT **DISTRACTED** AND DIDN'T GET MUCH DONE AT THE SANCTUARY...

THAT WAS BECAUSE YOU **WEREN'T** THERE!

AND IT WASN'T EVEN **YOU** WHO SAID IT!

"THAT'S WHY, THIS MORNING, YOU - I MEAN **HE**..."

"THE CHAMELEON, DISGUISED AS YOU!"

"THAT'S WHY **HE** WASN'T WEARING GLASSES."

WHICH MEANS...

HE WAS THE ONE WHO SWITCHED THE GEM-KEYS.

HE WAS THE ONE WHO BROUGHT MUM TO THE RAINFOREST REALM.

"HE WAS THE ONE WHO GOT HER **BITTEN!**"

ALL OF IT, JUST TO GET THE GUARDIAN-KEY!

"AND NOW **THEY** HAVE IT!"

"SO, WHAT ARE WE GOING TO DO?"

"WE'RE GOING TO GET IT BACK."

"AND WE'RE GOING TO FIND THAT CURE."

OKAY, TAKE IT EASY.

SO LONG AS WE'RE *CAREFUL* AND *QUIET*, WE WON'T GET SPOTTED.

OKAY, THERE'S ONE THERE.

WE JUST HAVE TO STAY *HIDDEN*.

STICK TO THE PLAN.

AND *DEFINITELY* STICK TOGETHER THIS TIME!

GWG

WHAT *IS* THAT?

THE GUARDIAN-KEY!

IT LOOKS LIKE THE DOOR THING AT THE SANCTUARY!

A PORTAL.

"WAIT."

"WHERE'S JAK?"

"HE'S *UP* THERE!"

"BOTH OF HIM!"

"WE HAVE TO HELP HIM!"

KICK

LOOK OUT!

GRRRR

ROW-RAAW

THANKS!

THAT WAS *CLOSE!*

URGH!

JAK!

ARE YOU *OKAY?*

I'M ÷COUGH COUGH÷ *SO* SORRY, EVERYONE.

THIS ÷COUGH÷ THIS IS ALL *MY* FAULT.

"I NEED TO MAKE IT *RIGHT.*"

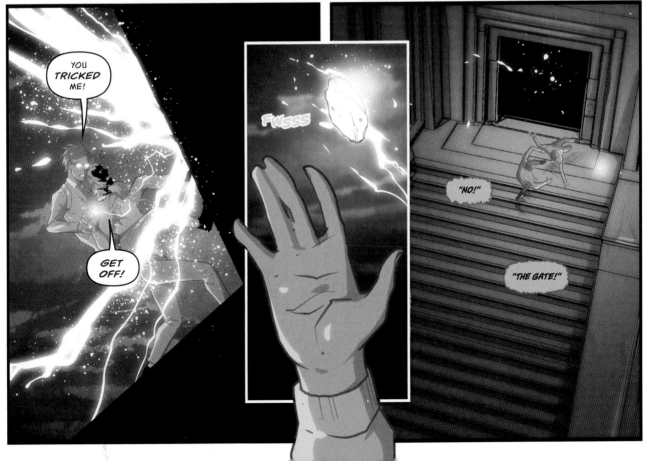

KA-SMASSSH

SMAKK

UNLUCKILY FOR YOU, *VOID BEAST*, WE WERE ABLE TO GET ONE OF THE OLDER SPARE WEAPONS BACK AT THE SANCTUARY WORKING.

THIS IS FOR *DAGAH!*

AND FOR *MUM!*

NOOOooooo...

FOOM!

EVERYTHING'S GOING TO BE OKAY.

I LOVE YOU, MUM.

I LOVE YOU TOO, SON.

NOW, GUARDIAN-KEY...

WHERE IS IT?

OH!

"WE... WE LOST IT..."

"IT'S STILL IN THE RAINFOREST REALM."

WITH JAK.

WE, ERM, WE... WE LOST HIM TOO.

"HE'S THE ONE WHO CLOSED THE DOOR."

"HE STOPPED THE VOID BEASTS GETTING THROUGH."

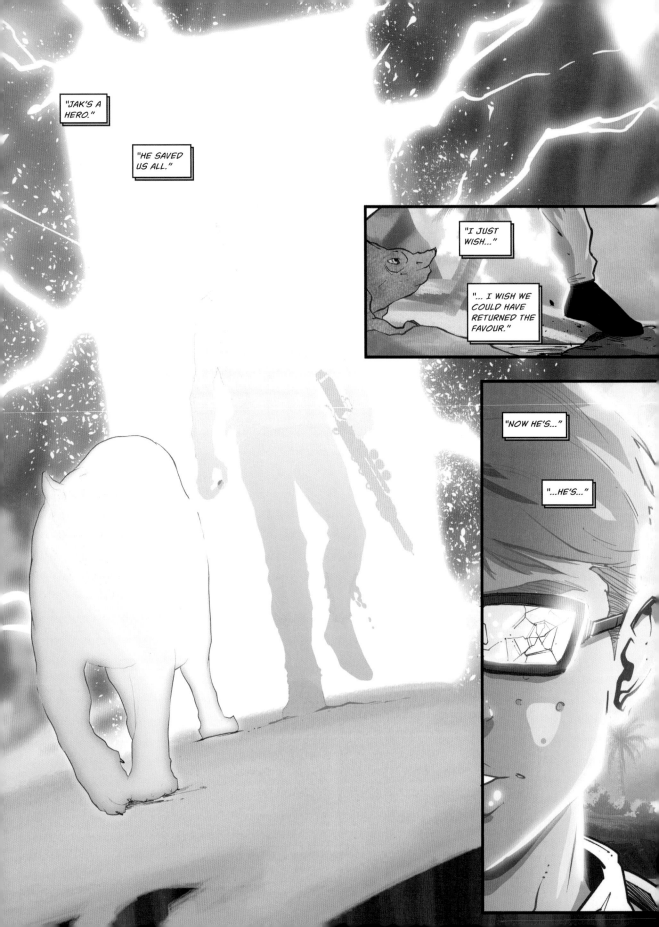

...HERE?

JAK'S *HERE?*

SORRY WE'RE A BIT LATE.

WE HAD A FEW *THINGS* TO DEAL WITH BEFORE WE COULD GET AWAY.

SOMEONE HERE'S GOT SOMETHING TO SAY.

YES, I'M VERY, *VERY* SORRY ABOUT WHAT HAPPENED, EVERYONE.

I KNOW IT'S NO EXCUSE, BUT I... I WAS *BITTEN* YOU SEE... I WASN'T *REALLY* IN CONTROL OF MYSELF...

WAIT, BUT *HOW* DID Y-?

A VOID BEAST SMASHED THROUGH THE FOUNTAIN.

ONLY SHE WAS REALLY A BITTEN SLOTH BEAR - *MELURSUS URSINUS* - AND THE WATER TURNED HER BACK.

THE BEAR AND THE JAGUAR HERE STARTED FIGHTING VOID BEASTS *TOGETHER.*

THEY DRAGGED MY *EVIL TWIN* INTO THE FOUNTAIN AND CURED HIM.

THEN, THE ONES WE *COULDN'T* CURE, I *BLASTED* WITH THE WEAPON KYLE DROPPED.

OH YEAH, AND I... I BROUGHT *THIS* BACK.

HERE.

A FEW DAYS LATER...

BEEP

HEY, GUYS!

REMEMBER ME?

I KNOW IT HAS BEEN A REALLY, *REALLY* LONG TIME SINCE I WENT LIVE, SO I WANTED TO SAY SORRY FOR THAT.

THE NEW PLACE WE MOVED TO DIDN'T EVEN HAVE *WI-FI* UP UNTIL THIS MORNING, SO...

...YEAH, THINGS HAVE BEEN *CRAZY!*

I MEAN... YEAH... *SO* CRAZY.

LIKE, YOU *LITERALLY* WOULD NOT BELIEVE NINETY-NINE PER CENT OF IT.

HONESTLY, I'M NOT EVEN SURE *I* DO.

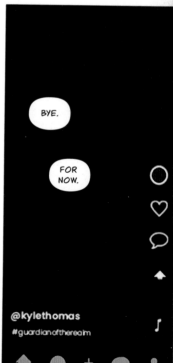

My first thank you goes to you for purchasing my book. I hope you enjoyed it as much as I have loved working on it!

Thank you to my loyal followers, your support and love means the world and has given me the opportunity to work on incredible projects.

A big thank you to Alan Samuel at Spotlight Management, who has been a remarkable manager. Alan has consistently helped me to turn my passions into hugely exciting, life-changing projects.

Thank you to Lauren Gardner at Bell Lomax Moreton, who structured my initial ideas and introduced me to team Penguin and the phenomenal Daniel Bunyard, without whose encouragement and faith in me this project could not have been executed.

It has been a pleasure working with the exceptionally talented Amrit Birdi, who brought my vision and characters to life through his breathtaking illustrations, thank you.

Thank you to Leah Moore and John Reppion, who have also been a pleasure to work alongside. They understood every one of my ideas from the offset and used their talented writing skills to give this project structure and substance.

I will also take this opportunity to thank my parents, family and friends. Especially my mum, without her this journey would have never begun. Thank you, Mum, for being my support and inspiration. I am eternally grateful for you. Thank you for sharing such a passion for animals with me; I cannot wait for all of our future adventures together.

KYLE THOMAS

Kyle Thomas was born in Kent, England and is now based in Belfast, Ireland with his mum. Kyle has stormed the internet with his entertaining videos and is a TikTok phenomenon with an astounding following of over 30 million, along with a hugely popular Instagram page of 1 million followers. Kyle is incredibly well-loved for his entertaining and awe-inspiring videos that feature Kyle's pet meerkat Mylo, along with his other extraordinary rescue animal friends.

WRITING KYLE THOMAS'S GUARDIAN OF THE REALM

BY LEAH MOORE & JOHN REPPION

When we got the opportunity to work with Kyle Thomas and Amrit Birdi on *Guardian of the Realm*, we absolutely jumped at the chance. We've been writing comics as Moore & Reppion for almost twenty years now. Our first ever series together – *Wild Girl* – was all about a teenage girl with the power to talk to animals. Our 2018 book *Conspiracy of Ravens* (co-created with artist Sally Jane Thompson) was about an English schoolgirl discovering she had magical powers, all bound up in the folklore of ravens and birds. So, we knew straight away that Kyle's love of animals, and his rapport with Mylo, would be at the heart of this new story. With Amrit's amazing art, we knew we'd be able to take things up a notch, and make the animals, and the magical realms they inhabit, really leap off the page.

The idea of starting out with dull, monochrome colours was to reflect Kyle's worry and uncertainty about the big change of moving to the Sanctuary. As we get further and further into the story, and Kyle's knowledge and confidence grows, things become more and more bright and colourful.

Life can feel like that sometimes, especially when you're facing something new like moving house, or starting at a new school. Things can seem gloomy and frightening, but it's important to know that there's always a brighter day somewhere ahead.

Guardian of the Realm is an action-packed adventure, but it's also all about change. About the challenges we all face when we find ourselves starting a new chapter of our lives and having to make new friends. It can be scary and difficult, but it can also be really rewarding. An opportunity to find a new you, and a new future. *Guardian of the Realm* is also all about family. About how Kyle and his mum and Mylo are a solid, unbreakable unit who can all rely on each other no matter what life throws at them. Everyone needs that special someone they can always count on, be that a parent, a pet, a friend, or someone else. They're the people who love and care for you no matter what, and, sometimes, finding them can be a challenge in itself. But it's a challenge worth rising to. It's a risk worth taking. To believe in yourself, and to find someone who believes in you and supports you, is really what life is all about.

It's been brilliant working with Kyle, Amrit, and the whole team on this book. We really hope you had as much fun reading *Guardian of the Realm* as we did writing it.

Leah Moore is a writer, born in Northampton, England. Since 2003 she has co-written comics and graphic novels with her husband, John Reppion, as Moore & Reppion. Their 2018 Middle Grade magical adventure *Conspiracy of Ravens* (co-created with artist Sally Jane Thompson) was published by Dark Horse Comics. Leah has worked with world famous recording artists The Doors, Mötley Crüe, Joan Jett and others on music-themed graphic novels published by Z2 Comics.

John Reppion is a writer, born in Liverpool, England. Since 2003 he has co-written comics and graphic novels with his wife, Leah Moore, as Moore & Reppion. Their 2018 Middle Grade magical adventure *Conspiracy of Ravens* (co-created with artist Sally Jane Thompson) was published by Dark Horse Comics. John's comics work has appeared in the likes of *2000 AD, Heavy Metal* magazine and *Monster Fun*.

BEHIND THE SCENES: THE TEAM

ILLUSTRATOR & ART DIRECTOR

Amrit Birdi is a bestselling illustrator and comic artist, most widely known for illustrating Joe Suggs's *Username: Evie* series (Hodder & Stoughton) and *Alex Rider: Ark Angel* (Walker Books). Day-to-day, Amrit is the art director of London-based AmCo Studio. He and his team produce graphic-novel art, concept art, storyboards, promotional art, commercial illustration and animation for end-clients such as Disney, Netflix, Amazon, Square Enix, Adobe, Bandai/Namco, Adidas, Macmillan, Ubisoft and more.

You can keep up to date with him on Instagram (@amrit_birdi_).

amco-studio.com

TONES & ASSISTS

Madelaine Salvage has a great eye for detail and assists on the tonal work and adding shadows and highlights to the art.

She straddles being both a writer and artist fantastically well, making her the perfect person to help with visual storytelling.

DIGITAL PAINTER

Palash Sasmal is an up and coming digital artist based in West Bengal.

Undertaking study at the Government College of Art and Craft in Calcutta, he is now a specialist in background and environment art.

COMIC LETTERER

Rob Jones is a freelance, UK-based award-nominated writer and award-winning letterer of comic books.

He has lettered various books from Image, Humanoids, Heavy Metal, Scout and many, MANY more.

BEHIND THE SCENES: ART PROCESS

1 SCRIPT SAMPLES

Pages Ninety-Six & Ninety Seven
These two pages are opened out into one widescreen double page spread, so I'm going to script them that way.

There are three tiers – each one running the whole width across both pages – and they each have one large panel filling them.

There are six inset panels – two on each of those tiers: one falling on the right-hand page and one on the left-hand page. So, this spread has a total of nine panels.

Panel Three
This is the second inset panel on this tier, and it sits over to the left of page ninety-seven (though not hard up against the middle of the page). This is a shot of Jak pushing his way through the undergrowth towards us (maybe not quite full figure, his lower legs obscured by the thick vegetation. He isx holding the Guardian key in one hand, and the gem is glowing. He still has his glasses on his head. One of the butterflies from the larger, surrounding panel is crossing over into this one, so that the butterfly is an observer of what's happening – actually in the panel with Jak.

There are six speech captions across this entire two-page tier – three on each side.

Cap: "Okay, okay, listen, I guess it's time I explained some stuff to you."

Cap: "This place where we are, it's called a Realm."

Cap: "The Realms kind of sit next to our own world, but they're different."

Cap: "And crossing over into them makes people different."

Cap: "Here animals can talk."

Cap: "We can understand them, and they can understand us."

2 ART STEPS

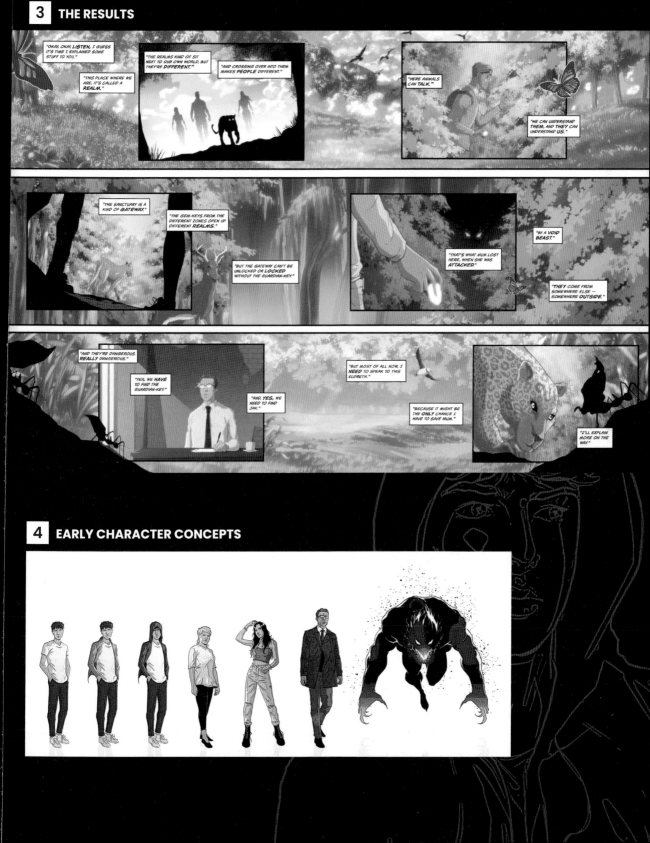

"OKAY, OKAY, LISTEN, I GUESS IT'S TIME I EXPLAINED SOME STUFF TO YOU."

"THIS PLACE WHERE WE ARE, IT'S CALLED A *REALM*."

"THE REALMS KIND OF SIT NEXT TO OUR OWN WORLD, BUT THEY'RE *DIFFERENT*."

"AND CROSSING OVER INTO THEM MAKES PEOPLE *DIFFERENT*."

"HERE ANIMALS CAN *TALK*."

"WE CAN UNDERSTAND THEM, AND THEY CAN UNDERSTAND US."

"THE *SANCTUARY* IS A KIND OF *GATEWAY*."

"THE GEM-KEYS FROM THE DIFFERENT ZONES OPEN UP DIFFERENT *REALMS*."

"BUT THE GATEWAY CAN'T BE UNLOCKED OR *LOCKED* WITHOUT THE GUARDIAN-KEY."

"THAT'S WHAT MUM LOST HERE, WHEN SHE WAS *ATTACKED*."

"BY A *VOID BEAST*."

"THEY COME FROM SOMEWHERE ELSE -- SOMEWHERE *OUTSIDE*."

"AND THEY'RE DANGEROUS. *REALLY* DANGEROUS."

"YES, WE *HAVE* TO FIND THE GUARDIAN-KEY."

"AND, *YES*, WE NEED TO FIND JAX."

"BUT MOST OF ALL NOW, I *NEED* TO SPEAK TO THIS ELDRETH."

"BECAUSE IT MIGHT BE THE *ONLY* CHANCE I HAVE TO SAVE MUM."

"I'LL EXPLAIN MORE ON THE WAY."

4 EARLY CHARACTER CONCEPTS

PENGUIN MICHAEL JOSEPH

UK | USA | Canada | Ireland | Australia
India | New Zealand | South Africa

Penguin Michael Joseph is part of the Penguin Random House group of companies
whose addresses can be found at global.penguinrandomhouse.com

First published 2022
001

Colour reproduction by AltaImage Ltd
Printed in Germany by Mohn Media

The authorized representative in the EEA is Penguin Random House Ireland,
Morrison Chambers, 32 Nassau Street, Dublin D02 YH68

A CIP catalogue record for this book is available from the British Library

ISBN: 978-1-405-95217-0

www.greenpenguin.co.uk

MIX
Paper from
responsible sources
FSC
www.fsc.org   FSC® C018179

Penguin Random House is committed to a
sustainable future for our business, our readers
and our planet. This book is made from Forest
Stewardship Council® certified paper.